AVER-RIDGE HIGH

1

...And don't forget that in celebration of the new double-decker bus of the Aver-Ridge Apes football team,

A pep rally will occur this Friday, so don't forget to wear your spirit colors: brown and darker brown.

For students with extra-curricular activites,

some minor changes have occured.

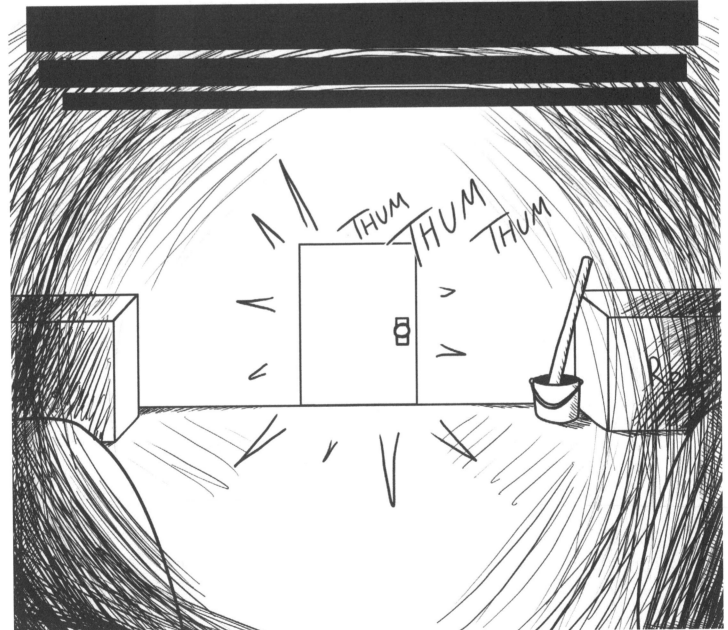

Q. Which of the following statements is most true?

A. 1. Scout Finch is a girl.
2. Boo Radley lives in a house.
3. Anatidaephobia is the fear that somewhere, somehow, a duck is watching you.
4. MOCKINGBIRDS!!

Yes, Sophie?

This question makes no sense!

Just try your best.

But it makes no sense!

Sophie! I've had enough of your lack of respect!

No one has a problem but you!

Is it wrong to actually *want* to learn something?

7

9

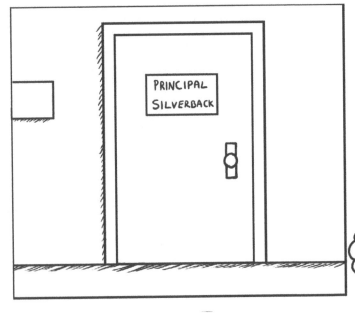

The alarm's going and he's still not back...

...should I stay or should I leave?...

These two...

...they didn't blindly follow the rest of the herd...

Maybe...maybe there is hope for them...

You know, I can't get enough of these!

Students!

Why are you still inside?

19

37

You can make every day Christmas by remembering ten easy tips.

1. You can never have too many toys. If you're feeling sad, buy some more.

2. A round belly is a happy belly. Remember, "sweets" rhymes with "eats"

3. Asking questions will only suck the magic out of life.

39

Back in Blissville

You're the only one for me, baby.

Hi, I'm looking for Santa Clause.

You should ask the mayor. He knows everything!

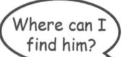

Where can I find him?

You should ask the mayor. He knows everything!

Did you hear me?

(I think this one's broken.)

41

44

...Or the fortune-tellers.

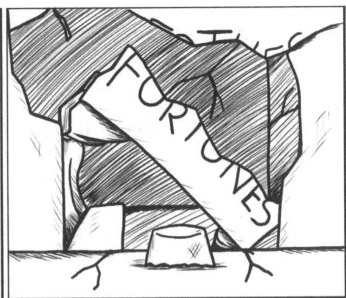

GRRRR

It's not my fault that none of it was real.

PING

Wait a second. Is any of this real?

CRACKLE

Void question. One can only ask how.

Ok...um...how are we here?

Eighteen years ago, your parents decided to...

Ok, ok, never mind.

We're not going to get the right answers unless we ask the right questions.

Where are we?

We are in the realm of Philosophy.

What is Philosophy?

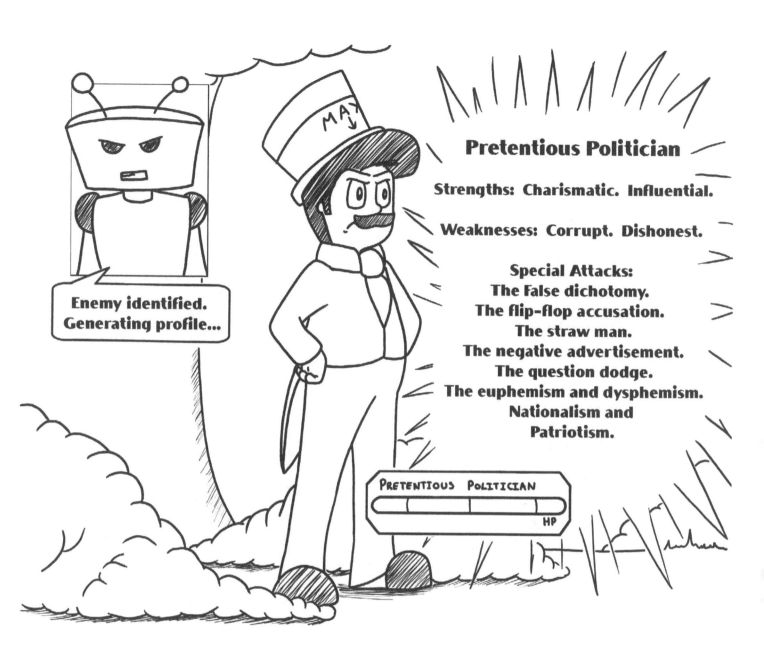

Where are we headed, Uck?

Running away always leads back to Blissville.

STOP SCREECH TRIP

What should we do?

Ow!

Vanquish the enemy.

65

66

68

Yes.

Uck, is this battling business going to be a common occurrence?

Sweet!

Why?

There are many who will try to prevent you from finding the key to life.

But why?

ACTIVATING "PHIL MODE"

Because they suck at life.

Oh. So the reason to study Philosophy is so that you don't suck at life?

Affirmative. And to learn how to resist those that do.

I think I can do that.

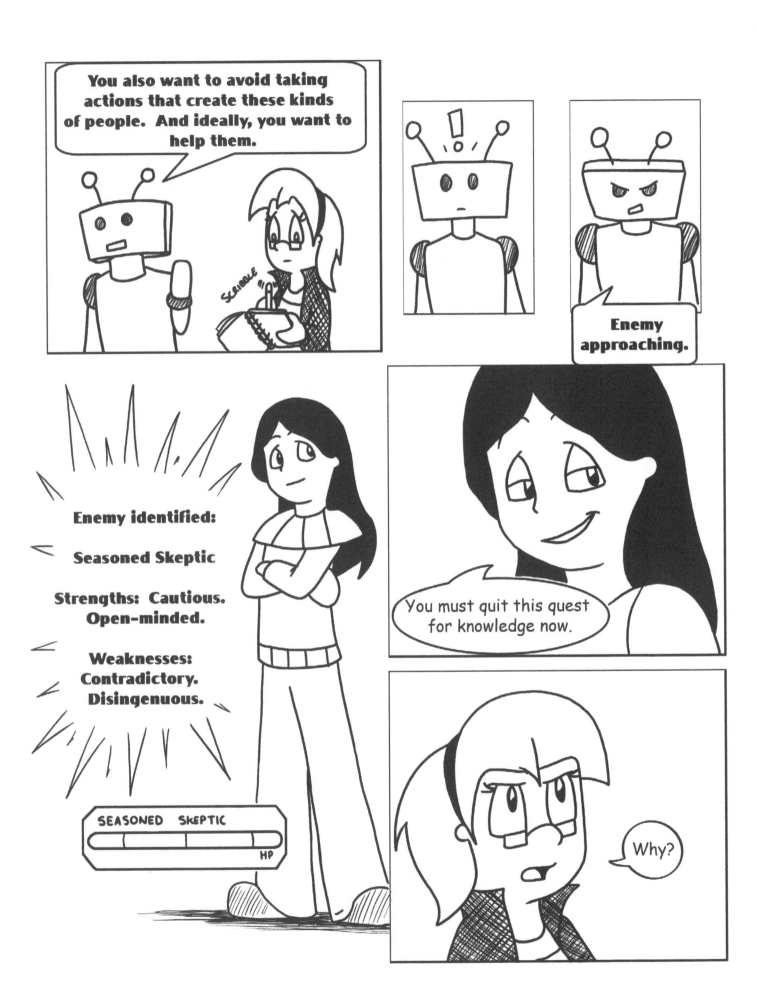

Why are there people like him?

-VOID ~~

Improper question.

Sorry.

How do people get to be like him?

This disease is most common among students of philosophy. They learn that they can argue anything and take pleasure in frustrating others with their ability to do so.

But what is the point of philosophy if you can argue anything?

Although it is true that one can argue anything, it is not true that all arguments are of equal value. The purpose of philosophy is to distinguish good arguments from bad arguments.

Will you teach us how to do that?

Yes.

OK, I get it.

In Philosophy, the term "argument" simply means reasons to believe that something is true.

There are two types of arguments: deductive arguments and inductive arguments.
Deductive arguments seek to guarantee the truth of their conclusions...

OK, you're losing me.

For example, the following argument is a deductive argument.

ALL MEN ARE MORTAL.
SOCRATES IS A MAN.

THEREFORE, SOCRATES IS MORTAL.

A deductive argument is valid if the truth of the premises guarantees the truth of the conclusion.

I thought valid just meant good.

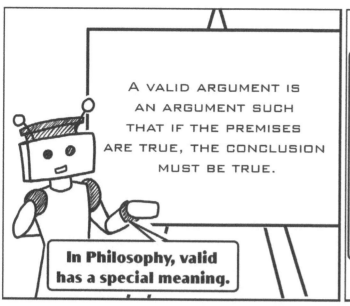

A VALID ARGUMENT IS AN ARGUMENT SUCH THAT IF THE PREMISES ARE TRUE, THE CONCLUSION MUST BE TRUE.

In Philosophy, valid has a special meaning.

Remember the argument I gave you about Socrates:

All men are mortal.
Socrates is a man.

Therefore, Socrates is mortal.

Is it valid? In other words, if the premises are true, must the conclusion be true.

Well, I don't know who this Socrates guy is.

You don't need to yet. The first step is to check for validity, which is essentially checking to see if an argument is in the proper form.

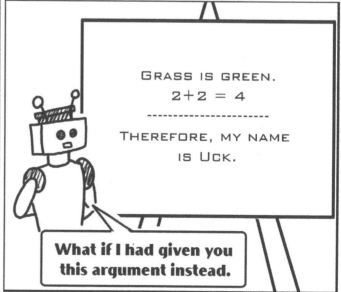

GRASS IS GREEN.
2+2 = 4

THEREFORE, MY NAME IS UCK.

What if I had given you this argument instead.

85

Woah.

Is that a good argument?

Um...no.

Why not?

Because the premises have nothing to do with the conclusion.

Correct.
If you are facing an invalid argument, you don't need to go any further than to point out that it is invalid. In the example I gave you, it would be silly to challenge the argument by questioning whether 2+2 really does equal 4 or whether grass really is green.

I get it. The first step is to see if an argument is valid. If it's not valid, there's nothing else to talk about.

Was my argument about Socrates valid?

If the first step is met, there is a second step.

Oh, right, a second step, I knew that.

The next step is to ask whether the premises are true.

Well, I am named Phil... but hey, not all people named Phil are idiots!

Correct. That argument was valid, but not sound.

Sound?

ALL MEN ARE MORTAL.
SOCRATES IS A MAN.

THEREFORE, SOCRATES IS MORTAL.

A sound argument is a valid argument with true premises, like the example I first provided.

A sound argument can never have a false conclusion, because the conclusion follows from the premises, and the premises are true.

So sound arguments are good arguments?

The fact that the sun has risen every day prior to today makes it very probable, though not completely certain, that the sun will rise tomorrow. Since the truth of the premise makes the conclusion quite probable, one could describe this inductive argument as strong.

So, are there weak inductive arguments too?

Yes. Can you think of one?

How about this?...

The last three drivers to cut me off were women. Therefore, all women are bad drivers.

Good. That is weak indeed.

If you say so...

We get it, Uck. I assume that analyzing an inductive argument is also a two-step process? First, is the argument strong or weak? If it is weak, it can be ignored; if it is strong, we ask whether the premises are true.

91

92

95

David Hume Born: 1711 Famous Empiricist

98

99

It's your turn now.

:¡@#***!!!**@w#***

!!*@@#**!!!

Should we say something?

It's none of our business

But if we don't say something

Then we won't get our butts kicked?

So you're saying we're better off staying out of it?

Yup.

But aren't we better off being true to ourselves and defending what we believe in?

Not if we defend our position poorly. That might be worse than not saying anything at all.

Have some confidence. Why do you think you'd do it poorly?

I'm not good with confrontation. I'll be awkward..

So you wish you were better at it?

Yeah, I guess so.

You can't get better without practicing.

But we're not going to change their minds.

How do you know?

Because they're drunk racists.

You never know. Maybe at a minimum we can convince them to be quiet drunk idiots.

Good luck with that.

Well, what about the other people here? We can at least set a good example for them by not keeping quiet.

Go for it!

Your'e not going to back me up?

How 'bout I back you up with some awesome music on the jukebox?

You're hopeless.

WOOow Phil, you're REALLY hopeless...

Come on, dude... this is a great song!

Is there such a thing as a great song? Or is music, and perhaps all of art, subjective?

Subjective?

Believing it's true makes it true. Like taste. You don't argue with people for not liking Arnie Palmers, do you?

Sometimes.

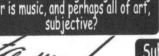

One day he was taking it out for a drive when he parked it near the end of a railway siding.

He started walking up the track, when he noticed a runaway train headed for a small child in its path.

The child was too far away to warn, but he could flip a switch that would divert the train onto a new path.

Unfortunately, doing so would result in his Bugatti getting smashed.

So Bob decided not to throw the switch, and the child was killed.

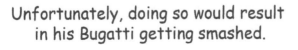

118

Hey Uck, I wanna learn how to do the right thing. Is there a list somewhere or something?

A list of what?

All of the right things to do.

Negative.

How could there be a list like that? Think of how long it would have to be!

Why?

Enemy approaching.

Enemy identified.

Emotional Enforcer

Strengths: Spontaneous. Exciting.

Weaknesses: Unstable. Unreliable. Inconsistent.

Special Attacks:
Defensiveness
Emotions *are* Reasons
Wishful Thinking

EMOTIONAL ENFORCER

HP

Did I hear someone say they were looking for an ethical compass?

Yep. Do you know where I can find one?

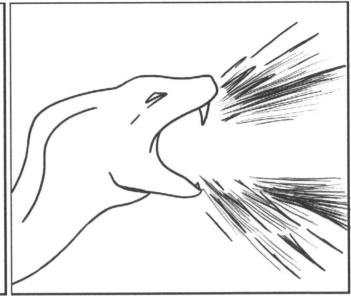

123

125

EMOTIONAL ENFORCER
HP

Affirmative.

It's okay to feel, but you shouldn't act on feelings unless you have reasons to.

That makes sense.

I mean, feelings could never be enough, because we don't feel anything for people or animals that we don't know...

...but that doesn't mean we can do whatever we want to them.

133

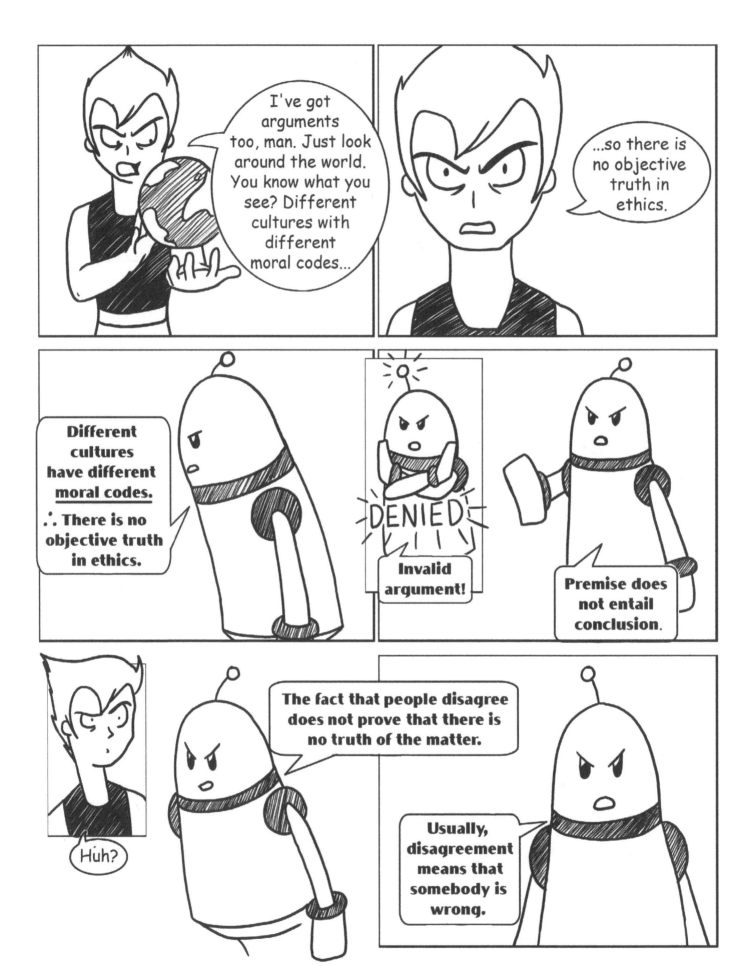

138

For example, if people start believing that 2+2=27,435.92, that won't prove that there is no objective truth in math. Rather...

...those people will be wrong.

RECKLESS RELATIVIST

HP

Okay, but that's math.

If people start believing that the world is flat, that won't prove that there is no objective truth in geography.

Again, those people will be wrong.

But ethics is different.

How so?

There are no proofs in ethics.

141

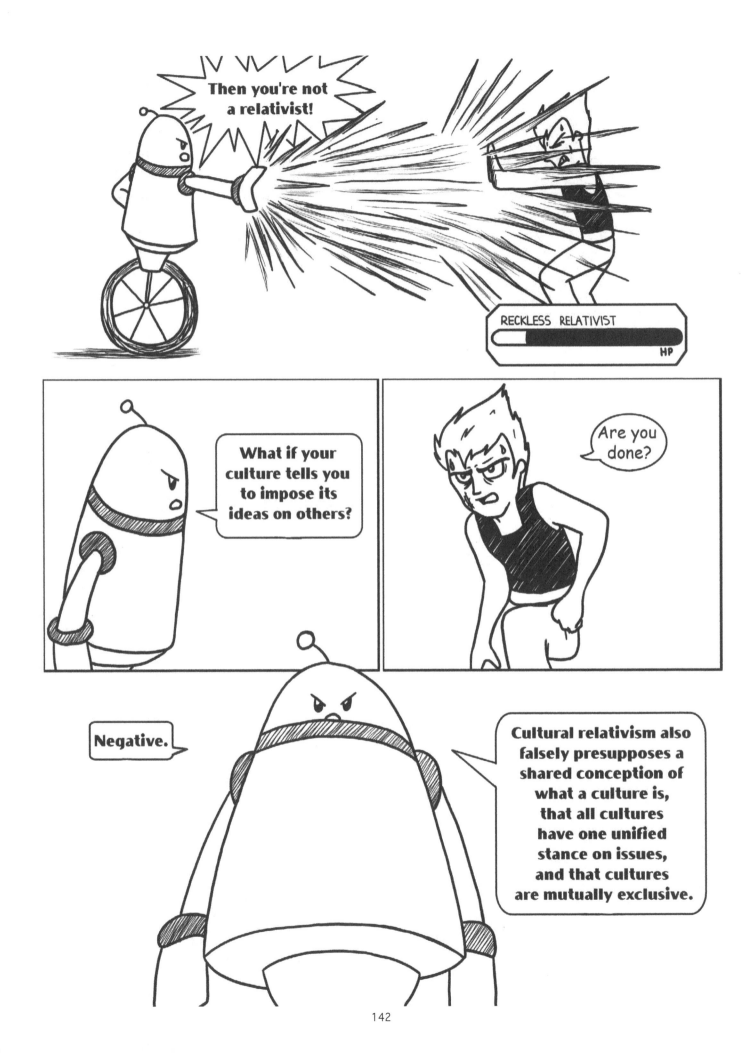

145

How did you find us?

We place tracking devices on everyone who enters our village.

Haven't you ever heard of the right to privacy?

Haven't you ever heard of security?

Haven't you ever heard of love?

Famous philosopher, logician, and pacifist

Author of "Why I'm not a Christian"

Awarded the Noble Prize in Literature

Bertrand Russell
Born 1872

CRASH

Hey!

Why are you helping them?

Ayn Rand
Famous Ethical Egoist
opposed to altruism.
Author of "The Fountainhead"
and "Atlas Shrugged"

What's in it for you?

Nothing. They needed help so I helped them.

You make me sick.

I don't get it.

He did the right thing, didn't he?

PAT PAT

You confused little boy.

I'm tired of trying to explain things to people like you...

...so just take this.

Phil acquires the Compass of Ethical Egoism!

Wow!

An ethical compass!

Thank you so much!

Just do me a favor and learn how to take care of yourself.

The compass will show you how.

No problem!

What a nice lady!

Socrates

Born: 469 B.C. Considered by many to be the Father of Western Philosophy. Famously stated that "the unexamined life is not worth living."

My friend Chaerephon went to Delphi and asked the oracle if there was anyone wiser than me.

The Pythian prophetess stated that there was no one wiser.

I was puzzled by this riddle, because I knew that I wasn't wise. So I set out looking for someone wiser than myself to refute the oracle.

I talked to the politicians, and after questioning them, I learned that they thought they were wise but weren't.

I went to the poets...

They were inspired, but not wise, though they thought they were.

I went to the artisans, and they did know things that I didn't.

Life is like an anvil!

But because they were good workmen, they thought they knew all kinds of high matters...

155

157

161

You could unhook yourself.

Uck...

Are you serious?

You aren't morally obligated to stay.

Ethical Egoism says:

It's in Sophie's self-interest to unhook...

...so she should.

Why are you looking at me like that?

Just because Uck said it was okay doesn't mean you should have done it.

That's what this is about?

You're jealous of Uck?

No...I...I... I just-

I just think you should make your own decisions.

Uck knows a lot more about Philosophy than we do.

Maybe, but I think he was wrong this time.

Why?

I don't know. It's hard to put it into words.

I guess I think that violinist had the right to live.

And what about me? Don't I have a right to my own body?

I guess so.

You guess so?

I mean, yes, you do.

I don't know.

I'm just sad he had to die.

Well, I don't think that dwelling on the past will help us find the key to life.

I'm not dwelling.

Just thinking...

I don't want to talk about this anymore, okay?

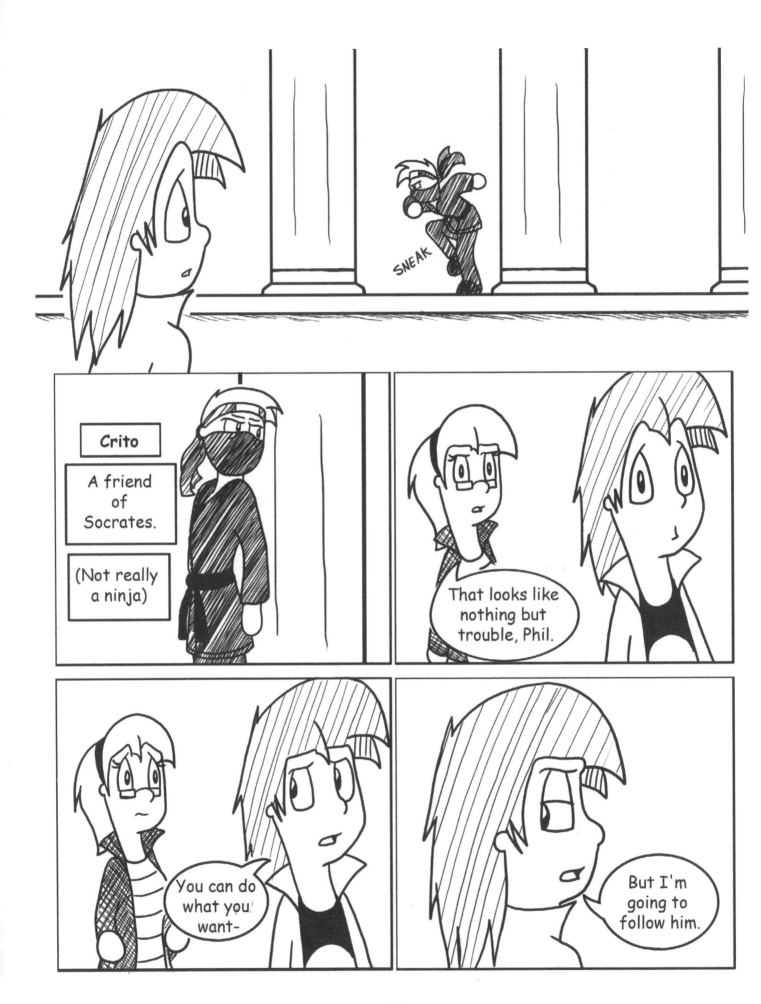

177

Next morning

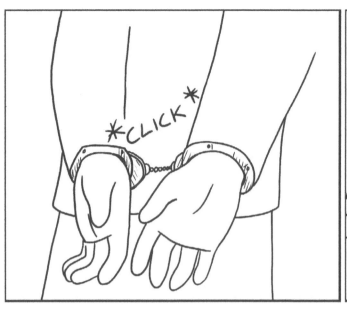

188

Enemy Identified.

The Pathetic Paper Writer

Special Attacks:
The Wishy Wash.
The Conclusion Sneak.
The Overdone Topic.
The Re-use.
The Book Report.
The Late Paper.
The Plagiarized Piece.

To get your friend through the judicial system, you'll need to know how to write well. Fortunately, I'm the master.

Allow me to educate you.

PATHETIC PAPER WRITER
HP

The first play you need to know is the wishy wash. People can't attack your position if you don't have one.

So just roll with phrases like; "this issue has been debated for centuries," "people have always questioned," "won't be resolved anytime soon," "we'll never know," etc.

Meander through your boring --I mean uncontroversial--paper for several pages, and then when they least expect it, in the final paragraph, hit them with something interesting and controversial.

Then end the paper suddenly, leaving them on that note.

What you do is take that controversial claim, move it to the first paragraph as your thesis statement, scrap everything else...

...and instead write a paper supporting that claim.

PATHETIC PAPER WRITER

HP

Then there's the book report.

Just throw as many facts on the page as you can. If you put enough words on the page, you're bound to do all right.

The goal is to support a claim with reasons, not to list irrelevant facts.

If you can't get all of that done on time, just use the late paper maneuver. It's especially effective when coupled with bad excuses.

Turn it in early. And even if you can't, you're better off turning in your decent paper on time than turning in a perfect paper late.

Not that late papers are usually perfect...

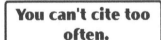

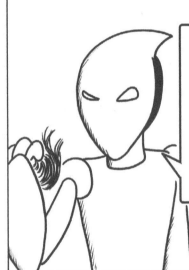

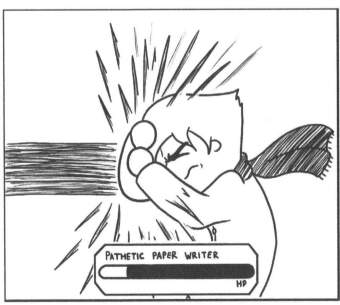

And you expect him to supplement that understanding with relevant (not overruled or inapplicable) case law, keeping current of the constant changes?

Yes.

And then you expect him to predict how a particular judge will interpret the law and apply it to a particular case when even attorneys can't do that perfectly?

...He needs to be punished.

Why?

Retribution, Deterrence, Incapacitation, and Rehabilitation.

Of course not.

Then how can a criminal deserve pain?

JADED JUDGE

HP

PLATO'S DIALOGUES

"What ignorant people deserve is to be educated."

Or think about it this way. Do you think people naturally get what they deserve?

I don't know.

If they do, there's no need for punishment.

And if not, isn't it possible that this guy's life has already been worse than he deserves?

You're making this too complicated. It's simple: an eye for an eye.

But that makes the whole world blind!

Mahatma Gandhi:
1869 - 1948
Was the preeminent leader of Indian nationalism in British-ruled India

205

Besides, you're not doing that.

How can you possibly take a physical act and convert it into a number of years in a cage?

We make our best guess.

So justice is just a guess?

I guess.

Why not do better than guess and just rape rapists and torture torturers?

That would be barbaric.

Jesus Christ

Central figure of
Christanity.
Believed to be
the son of God.

Yes.

Urgh

How can deterrence work when we agreed that crime isn't rational?

A person acting out of passion doesn't do a cost-benefit analysis.

Well...

Also, how could Phil be deterred when he didn't know the law?

He should of.

We went down that path already.

So the goal is to deter Phil from committing another crime?

Yes.

Look at him. This whole ordeal has shaken him up enough that it's not going to happen again.

Then forget deterrence, he must be incapacitated, separated from society so that he can't do any more harm.

He's not going to do any more harm if you let him go, but he is if you incarcerate him.

What do you mean?

Your taxpayers will have to pay a fortune to keep him locked up. You'll also be harming his friends, family, and everyone else who wants to see him do well.

I hadn't thought of that.

Did you think of this? If all you want is to incapacitate him, you have no justification for prison being painful rather than simply separate.

And if you let him go, we're out of here, so he will be separated.

I can't let him go without rehabilitating him first.

You really think that he can't cope in society?

He has proven that.

GLOMP

Sophie, that was amazing!

Just do me a favor and stay out of trouble.

I will.

If we avoid legal trouble, we shouldn't have to deal with any more jaded judges, right Uck?

Jaded judges come in other forms, such as parents and teachers who punish irrationally.

GLOOM

Oh.

That was amazing!

Enemy identified: Persistent Partygoer.

We should celebrate!

I dunno...I'm kind of--

PWEASE?

...

Fine, let's do it.

220

DEFEATED

Enemy Identified: Compulsive Collector.

What does she do?

Probably collects baseball cards, comics, beanie babies, recipes, cars, CDs, or movies. She then tries to convert this lead into gold by placing great value on these items.

But?

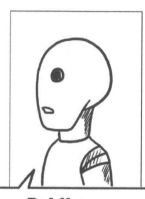

But they are still just items, which can't compare with knowledge and experiences.

Never mind. This is a particularly irksome variety of collector, the family photographer.

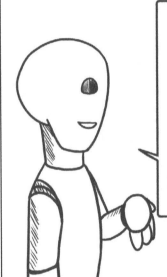

Boasting Braggart.

Special attacks: The one-up.

How does that work?

If you went to a foreign country, they went there twice. If you complain about a bad job you had, they had an even crappier one.

They are also masters of hyperbole.

Huh?

Gross exaggeration.

And false value.

False value?

The braggart may in fact have some very valuable experiences. Nevertheless, he overlooks that value and instead pursues things for the sake of gloating about them.

By making life a contest, the braggart ensures that he ends up losing.

So why does he do it?

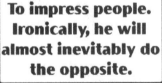

To impress people. Ironically, he will almost inevitably do the opposite.

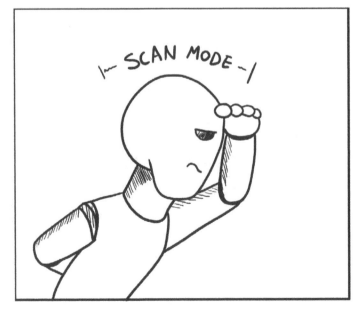

~ SCAN MODE ~

The Toilsome Talker.

I know some of these people. I've been hearing for years how they're going to move far away, or start their own business...

...or join the peace corps, or write a book.

What's wrong with setting goals?

They don't really set them, right Uck?

Affirmative. They simply want to be judged by their words rather than their actions... or inaction.

That's annoying.

Affirmative.

Do we have to do battle with all of them now?

Negative. It's important to pick your battles.

Why not call it a night?

But shouldn't we help them for their sake?

Care Ethics Compass says:

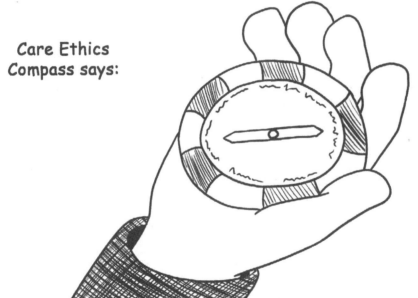

You don't have a duty to help these people because they are not in your close circle of family and friends.

Let's just go!

Not exactly.

They start with a situation where you'll believe a certain thing, and then they show you that a different situation is similar in all relevant respects, so you have to believe the same thing about that situation as well.

Huh?

Sigh

Take, for example, how you were kidnapped by the Music Lover's Society.

Most people would argue that you did not have a moral obligation to stay hooked up to the violinist.

Okay.

So some people, namely Judith Jarvis Thomson, would say this demonstrates to you that an abortion is sometimes morally acceptable.

You've completely lost me.

Even if it is granted that a fetus is a human being, and even if it is granted that human beings have a right to life...

...the violinist analogy proves that we don't believe that the right to live should trump someone's right to their own body.

Interesting...

So the first step in an argument from analogy is to see whether you get the intended reaction from your audience. If you both believed that there was a moral obligation to stay hooked up to the violinist, then there would be nothing more to talk about.

Right, and if we do have the intended reaction?

Then the second step is to see how accurate the analogy is. Are the two situations really similar in all relevant respects?

Well, one big difference is that I was kidnapped by the Society of Music Lover's. With most pregnancies, that's not how it works.

Right, so the analogy might still be effective to demonstrate the right to an abortion in cases of rape.

That makes sense, because in the rest of the cases, the woman has more or less invited the fetus to use her body.

So, by analogy, if somebody engages in activity that can result in pregnancy, that doesn't mean they invited the fetus, does it?

Hmm...

Especially if they took precautions.

Yeah, I guess that makes sense.

So that's how an argument from analogy works.

The first step is whether the arguer is right about the first situation, and the second step is whether the second situation is similar to the first in all relevant respects.

Not to criticize, but why go through the extra work? Why not just argue about the actual situations?

Sometimes people are too emotional or too stuck in a box about a situation, so it helps to take them out of that context so that can think about things more clearly.

. . .

I get it!

Enemy approaching.

Faithful Follower:

**Strengths:
Sincere,
Compassionate.
Weaknesses:
Irrational.
Overly confident.**

FAITHFUL FOLLOWER

HP

Just because somebody is religious doesn't make them an enemy of Philosophy, does it?

...

What is it about this character in particular that is so bad?

Special attacks:

Circular Arguments
Indoctrination.
"Literal" Interpretations.
The Leap of Faith.
Appeal to Ignorance.
Refusal to "Play God"
False Humility.

I guess I'm about to find out what all that means...

Do you have a minute to talk about God?

I do have some questions...

...but I'm sure it'll take more than a minute.

Phil is confused.
He hurt himself in his
confusion.

Phil fainted.

The Faithful
Follower is confusing
Phil with circular
arguments.

What's happening,
Uck?

Circular
arguments?

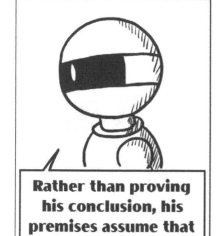

Rather than proving
his conclusion, his
premises assume that
the conclusion is true.

Essentially, he's using
his conclusion to prove
his conclusion. He may
as well have said "God
exists. Therefore, God
exists."

I get it.

Phil snapped out of his confusion.

You haven't proven anything!

Well, can you prove that God doesn't exist.

This is called the Appeal to Ignorance.

The fact that something hasn't been disproven doesn't prove that it's true.

The burden of proof is on him, and he's trying to unfairly shift it onto you.

Can you prove that magical talking ponies don't exist?

Um, no.

Well there you go. You still haven't proven anything.

Religious belief is not about proof; it's about faith.

What's faith?

Faith is confident belief in the absence of reason.

Why would anyone be confident about anything without reason?

245

Will you please just read the book? I think you'll like what it says.

Isn't what it says contingent upon who is interpreting it?

You don't need to interpret it.

Then why do so many different sects draw different teachings from the same text?

Some of them are getting it wrong.

Which ones?

Every sect that isn't his...

251

...

Moreover, is "don't kill" an absolute rule or more of a general guideline?

I'd say it's an absolute rule.

Really? Is it wrong to kill in self-defense?

Hmm...

FAITHFUL FOLLOWER

HP

Is it okay to kill people in a just war, if there is such a thing? What about the death penalty? Does this prohibit euthanasia?

Don't you see my point? When you answer these questions, you're doing so based on your own ability to reason...

...not based on the book that you're giving all the credit.

Maybe "don't kill" is a little vague...

...but what about "don't steal?"

But stealing is wrong!

Actually, I think that's pretty vague too.

Somebody stole my compass, and I tried to take it back. Was I stealing it?

Under the law you were.

So God's commandments actually mean we should do whatever our government says?

No, that doesn't seem right.

If I find abandoned property and take it, is that stealing?

I don't think so.

How do I determine if it's truly abandoned?

I dunno.

What about ideas? Can they be stolen? And if I borrow something with every intention of returning it, is that stealing?

Hmm...

FAITHFUL FOLLOWER

HP

Is downloading an electronic copy of a song stealing it?

Definitely.

You think that's what God had in mind?

I don't know.

Are taxes a form of stealing? What if I don't want my tax dollars to fund everything they go to?

I don't know what to tell you.

Is this an absolute rule too or just a guideline?

Absolute... I think?

So Robin Hood was unethical?

And what if I had to steal to save a life?

I get it! This is why you need an ethical compass and not a magic list.

Exactly. This guy doesn't have a compass, so he has no idea how to interpret this arbitrary set of rules.

I don't need to interpret it; I just read it literally.

But how do you know that's the right way to do it?

Well, I just believe it.

Even if a literal reading were possible, I doubt you'd do it all of the time.

Why do you say that?

Let me see that book...

"God hardened his heart."

"Knock and the door will be opened to you."

"If your right eye causes you to sin, gauge it out."

Hey!

Richard Dawkins

Born: 1941

Famous atheistic philosopher and scientist.

Faith is one of the world's greatest evils, like the smallpox but harder to get rid of.

Isn't that a little harsh?

When you divorce belief from evidence, you get suicide bombers killing themselves to get their 72 virgins. How do you stop that if reason is off the table?

I dunno.

I guess we need a "spiritual arms control," some highly trained theologians to lower the going rate in virgins.

I guess I see what you mean about the ridiculousness.

Parents are a big part of the problem. Raising a kid in a religion is a form of mental child abuse.

Child abuse?

You wouldn't talk about four-year old economic monetarists, neo-isolationists, or liberal Republicans, would you?

No.

Then how is it that we're okay with talking about a child as a Christian or a Hindu? We indoctrinate children into a religion without giving them a fair chance to make a rational choice.

I guess that's why so many people stay in the religion they were raised in.

I guess "faith" is the "F-word" of Philosophy, huh?

You could put it that way I suppose.

Are you an atheist?

I am.

What's that like?

You already know.

I do?

I think you're getting the hang of it. There's one other way to think about the Categorical Imperative: Never treat people solely as a means to an end.

Don't use people.

That's a bit different from the first formulation, isn't it Uck?

It generates the same principles: don't lie, steal, kill, etc.

I think I like this compass.

So Uck, back to the God question.

...

So you're the guy to talk to about God?

I guess I'm one of them.

William Paley, Born: 1743
Best known for the Teleological Argument
via the watchmaker analogy

So, what do you think?

What do **you** think?

271

Pretend that you'd never seen a watch before,

and you didn't know what one was or how it could be created.

Suddenly you stumble upon one as you're walking around.

What are you going to think?

What do you mean?

Well, are you going to think that the watch is the product of natural causes, like say, a rock, or are you going to think that someone must have created the watch?

Hmmm...

I think you're going to think someone created the watch just based on how orderly, complex, and even beautiful it is

It's significantly different from a rock.

I see what you're saying.

Now think about the universe, or if that's too big for you, the planet, the human body, or even a single cell.

Any of those are so substantially more orderly, complex, and beautiful than a watch is. So, by the same reasoning, don't you have to conclude that they were created?

Thomas Aquinas
Born: 1225
Famous theologian who argued
that God is the ultimate cause of
all things

Everything has a cause.

Either the chain of causes goes back forever...

...or there's a first, uncaused cause.

The chain of causes can't go back forever.

∴ There's an uncaused cause (i.e. God)

. . .

I don't get it!

Is he proving God's existence or Uck's existence?

Or is he saying Uck is God?

Why don't we find Uck and see what he knows?

Moments later...

What about the Cosmological Argument?

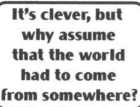

It's clever, but why assume that the world had to come from somewhere?

It just doesn't make sense to think about time existing for infinity.

But if you reject infinite causes because you can't conceptualize them, why would you jump to an infinite being, which is equally incomprehensible?

Besides, you're assuming that time is linear.

BOOM

WHOP

277

Are they?

Are the situations similar in all relevant respects?

Paley said the world is orderly, complex, and beautiful like a watch.

But some of the world is pretty ugly.

Or maybe beauty is subjective, merely in the eye of the beholder?

No, some people and things are just plain ugly.

But what are the odds of this world just coming together?!

What are the odds of God just coming together?

So the Cosmological Argument says that everything must have a cause, which begs the question "What caused God?"

And the Teleological Argument says that if something is great enough it must have been created, but then since God is the greatest it runs into the same problem, "What caused God?"

And if we're going to make an exception for God in either case, we might as well make an exception for something secular. So the arguments fail.

Affirmative.

But there must be other arguments for God!

There's the Argument from Religious Experience: God is real because he produces real effects.

How do we know he actually interacts with the world?

For every event, there are secular causes, so there is no need to jump to divine causes.

But what about when there isn't a clear cause, like a sick person miraculously getting better?

You can't credit God for miracles without blaming him for tragicals.

Tragicals?

When there's no clear explanation for something terrible that happens, is that God's doing too?

· · ·

I never thought of that.

Also, these claims tend to be circular: people start with the religion and then have the experiences that are consistent with their religion.

Is it any wonder that Christians have Christian experiences, whereas Hindus have Hindu experiences, etc? People see what they want to or expect to see

Oh. Well there must be other arguments.

Such as?

I don't know. There are so many religious people. They must have some good reasons.

Here's a quick test. Ask those people what would have to happen for them to stop believing. If the answer is nothing, then you know they aren't being rational about it.

291

I have an excellent reason for not intervening, but it's too complicated for you to understand.
You're nowhere near as smart as me, so trust me on this one. I'm a good person.
I'm a great cop, and I want people to freely believe that. If I'm always proving how awesome I am, then they're basically forced to believe it.
I don't want that.
What?
I just saved a woman last week! Do I have to intervene every time?
The fact that there aren't more tragedies like this one is testimony to my greatness.
It could have been much worse! He had a blowtorch with him, but I knocked it away. Sure, he still had the switchblade, pliers, and acid, but it could've been way worse without me there!
Here's a little secret. This body isn't really hers. I had her resuscitated and flown to a tropical paradise.
That's more than adequate compensation for that little bit of suffering she went through, so I'm still a greaty guy.

Those morons! Those are the most ridiculous reasons I've ever heard.

THEY'RE COMMON ONES.

Eh?

THINK ABOUT GOD. ON MANY CONCEPTIONS, HE IS ALL-GOOD, ALL POWERFUL, AND ALL-KNOWING, RIGHT?

Right.

SO THEN WHY IS THERE SUFFERING?

...

YOU CAN'T ANSWER WITHOUT GIVING ONE OF THOSE TWELVE ANSWERS OR ANOTHER EQUALLY POOR ONE, CAN YOU?

AND IT'S A LOT EASIER FOR GOD TO INTERVENE THAN A PERSON.

I guess not.

HE DOESN'T EVEN HAVE TO SNAP HIS FINGERS. SO WHAT DOES THAT MEAN?

296

What's with all the commotion?

I don't have to defend myself. The customer is always right.

Actually no.

Idiots don't magically become geniuses when they become customers.

But maybe I should treat her like she is.

Hell no!

You start doing that and you propagate the very behavior you want to get rid of.

But she sold the last wine amphora to another customer before I got here!

THE MISDIRECTED ATTACK.

You're getting mad at the wrong person. Besides...

ENEMY IDENTIFIED:
SELFISH SALESPERSON

STRENGTHS: ELOQUENT, APPROACHABLE
WEAKNESSES: DISINGENUOUS, IRRITATING

SPECIAL ATTACKS:
THE WARRANTY
THE REBATE
THE HIGH BALL
THE OVERREACTION
THE ABSENT AUTHORITY
THE DECOY
THE ADVERTISEMENT

ENEMY IDENTIFIED:
COMMON CONSUMER

STRENGTHS: GOAL DRIVEN. ENTHUSIASTIC
WEAKNESSES: WASTEFUL.SHALLOW. BRAINWASHED.
SPECIAL ATTACKS:
    THE UPGRADE
    THE SUPPLEMENT
    FALSE VALUE
    $ = ☺
    WORTH=POSSESSIONS

299

300

301

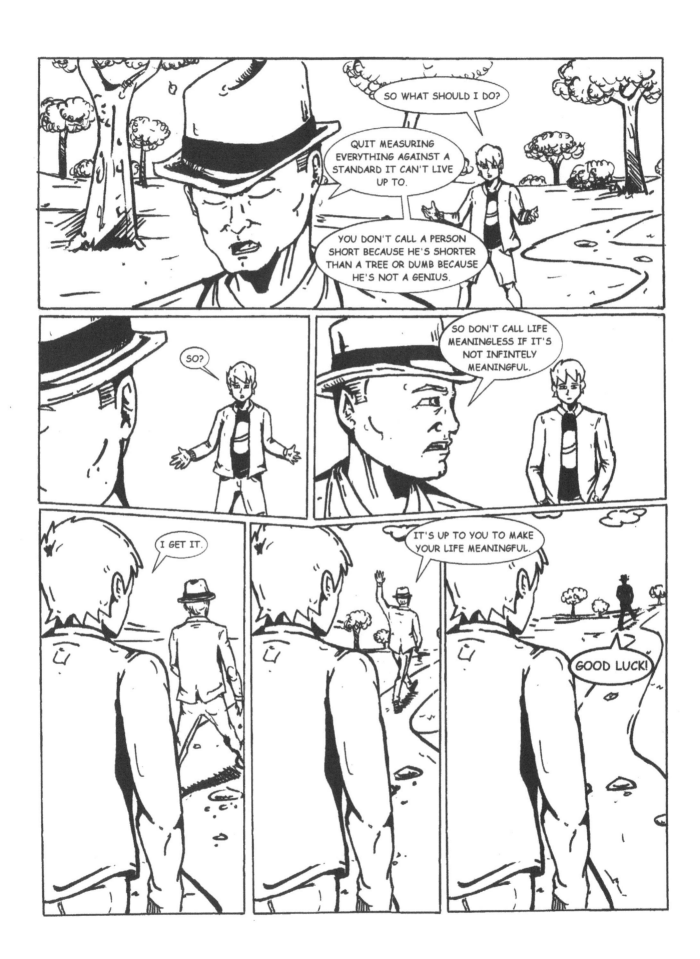

311

ROBERT NOZICK
BORN: 1938
FAMOUS LIBERTARIAN
PHILOSOPHER

Enemy identified:
Grasping Gambler

Strengths:
Willing to take
risks

Weaknesses:
Consumed.
Self-defeating

Special Attacks:
The Luck Card
The Gambler's Fallacy

UCK!

STAY OUT OF THIS MR. ROBOT.

BE CAREFUL, PHIL. THIS IS A DANGEROUS PLACE AND A DANGEROUS ENEMY.

I DON'T UNDERSTAND WHY I'M NOT WINNING, UCK.

CASINOS STAY IN BUSINESS BECAUSE THE ODDS ARE ALWAYS IN THEIR FAVOR.

BUT AFTER I KEPT LOSING, I FIGURED I WAS DUE FOR A WIN.

THAT'S THE GAMBLER'S FALLACY. IF YOU FLIP A COIN FIVE TIMES AND IT COMES UP HEADS EACH TIME, THE NEXT TOSS IS STILL 50/50.

IF EVERYTHING IS JUST STATISTICS, THEN HOW DO YOU EXPLAIN LUCKY PEOPLE?

I'M UNFAMILIAR WITH THIS MYSTICAL FORCE YOU CALL LUCK. DOES IT ENSURE THAT THE CARDS ARE SHUFFLED IN A WAY THAT WILL BENEFIT THE 'LUCKY' PERSON?

UH... MAYBE.

328

337

341

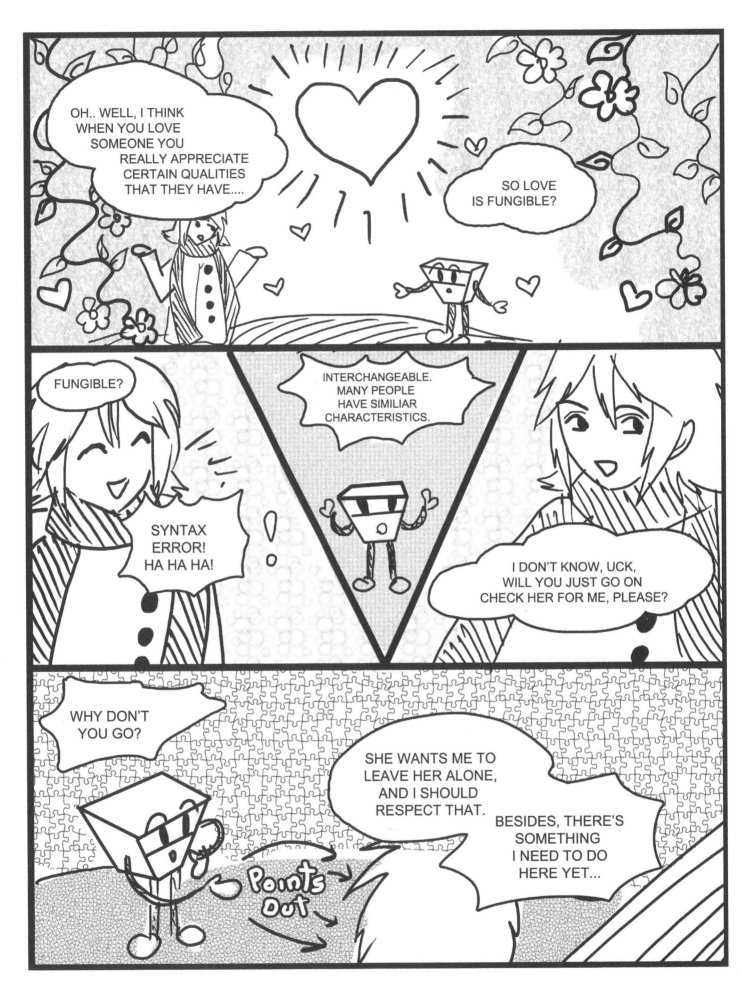

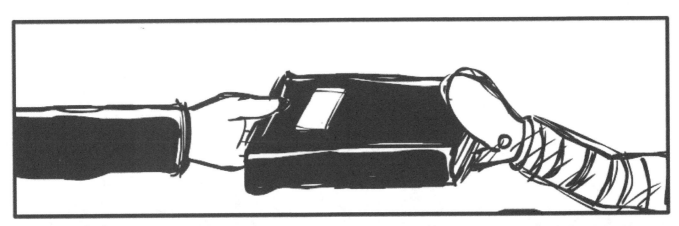

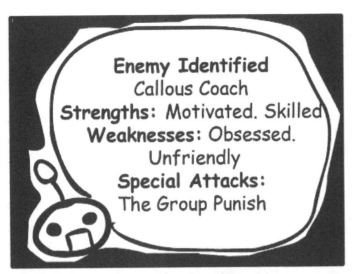

You can't deter somebody into performing better. If they're nervous, they'll do worse.

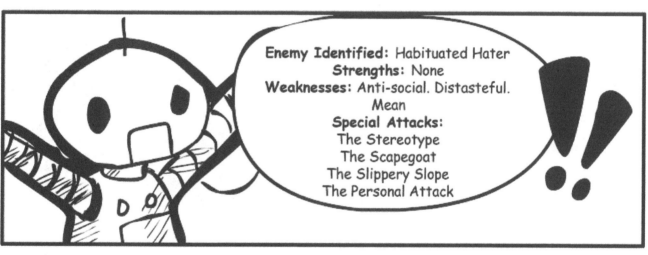

Enemy Identified: Habituated Hater
Strengths: None
Weaknesses: Anti-social. Distasteful. Mean
Special Attacks:
The Stereotype
The Scapegoat
The Slippery Slope
The Personal Attack

Nice shot. That guy was gay.

Homosexual?

No, you know, just a loser.

Okay, but it's not common!

Neither is being left-handed. Does that make left-handed-ness immoral?

SWOOOSH

Look, everything has a purpose, and the purpose of sex is reproduction!

I'm not sure why you'd assume everything has a purpose, or that everything has only one purpose.

That's just the way it is.

So the purpose of our eyes is seeing?

Duh.

So if I use them to communicate by winking that's immoral?

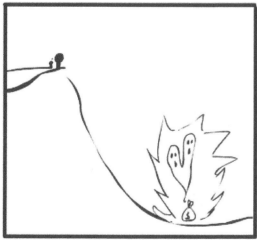

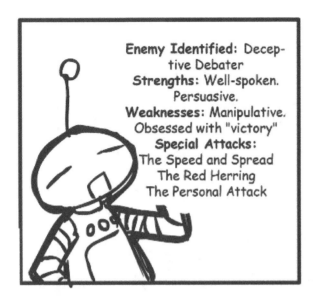

Enemy Identified: Decep-
tive Debater
Strengths: Well-spoken.
Persuasive.
Weaknesses: Manipulative.
Obsessed with "victory"
Special Attacks:
The Speed and Spread
The Red Herring
The Personal Attack

What does all that mean,
Uck.

With the speed and spread, she
tries to make as many points as
quickly as possible to present
the illusion of
a strong case.

Illusion?

The points may all be weak
or blatantly false, but the
idea is to impress with sheer
numbers and not give
people any time to focus on
particulars.

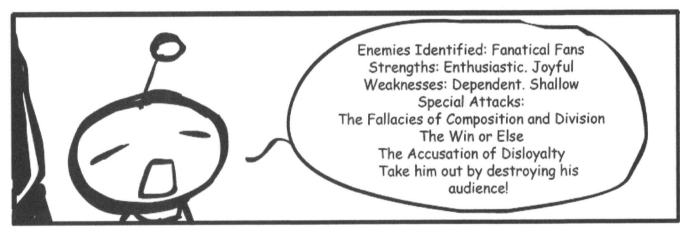

And how does a team earn your loyalty? By winning a lot?

BANDWAGON !!

Then what is it? Being from the same region as you are?

YAYYYYYY

But that's completely arbitrary. You're telling me that you have a random, unearned allegiance to professional players of a game, and you're proud of it?

SILENCE

Enemy Identifed: Professional Pleaser
Strengths: Kind, Considerate, Friendly.
Weaknesses: Uptight, Fake, Repressed.
Special Attacks:
The shapeshift, The Self-sacrifice, The
Compromise, TheSidestep

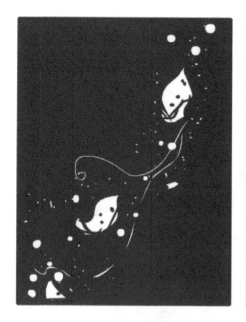

That was easy, but did you say that compromise was one of the attacks? Why is that bad?

First, it keeps people from reaching creative win-win solutions.

Okay, but what if there isn't one? Then shouldn't you compromise?

Maybe, but compromise only works if people are coming from equally reasonable positions.

HUH?!

Leo Tolstoy, Born: 1828

Famous novelist who wrote
War and Peace as well as Anna Karenina.

I'd have to say it's just a little worse than usual, wouldn't you?

It's just about the same.

What are you talking about?

The beast and dragon represent death, the inevitable fate that awaits us all.

The mice represent time, which is always working against us, bringing us closer to death.

The honey represents the good things in life, you know family, friends, hobbies.

Exactly. Once you realize the gravity of your situation, the inevitability of your own death, the honey no longer tastes sweet.

What's the third option?

3. The path of strength.

I like the sound of that!

To be strong is to end the stupid joke. Let go of the branch and face the dragon.

You mean kill yourself?

flap

Exactly.

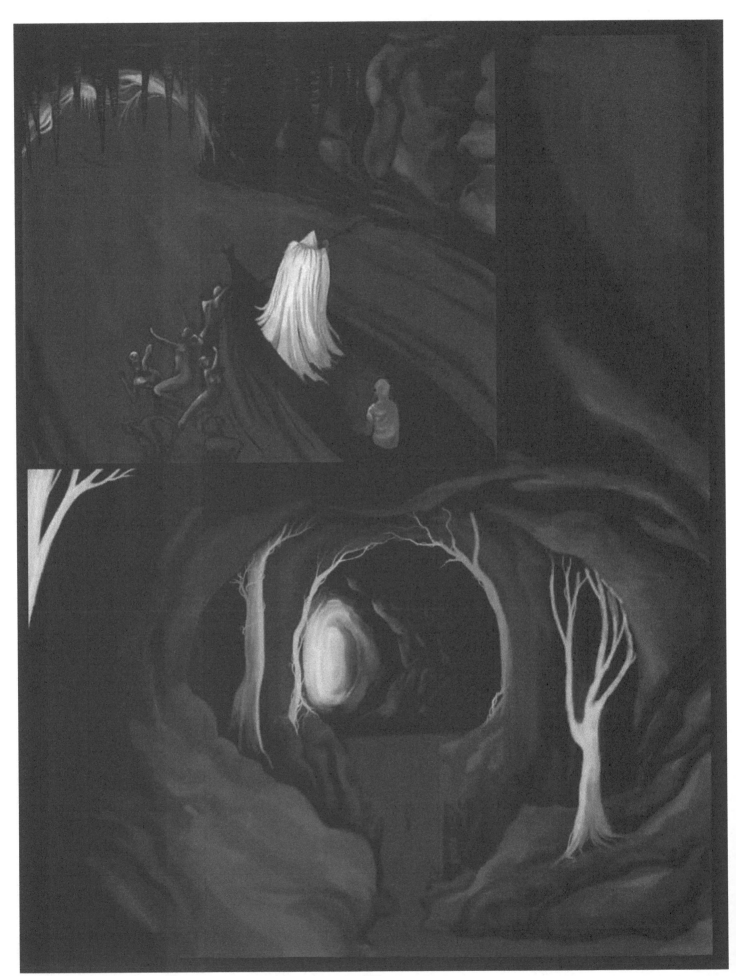

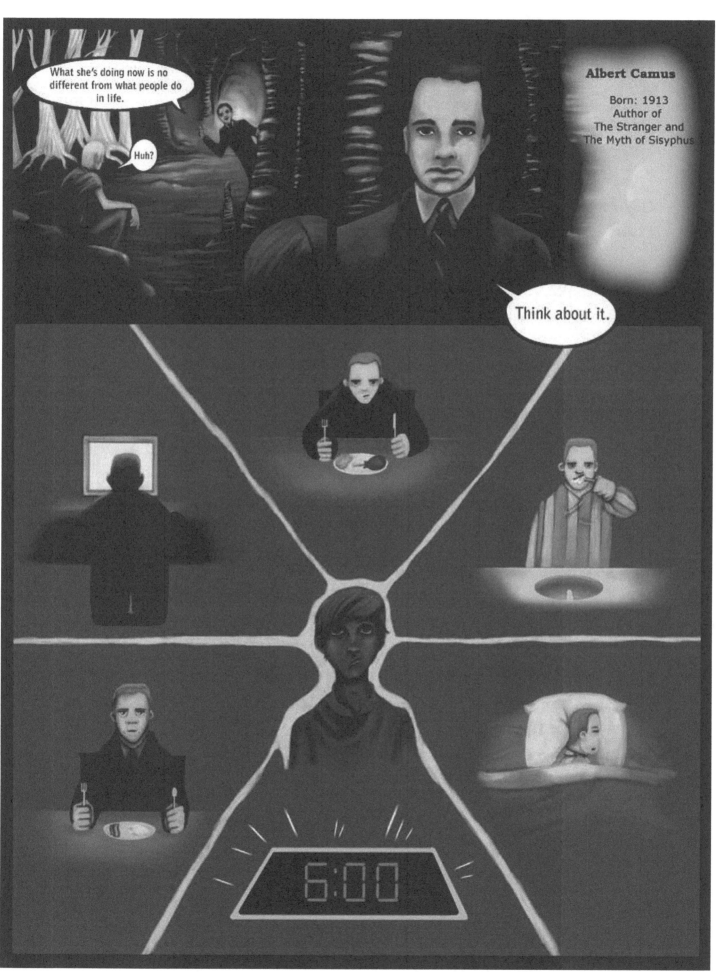

400

403

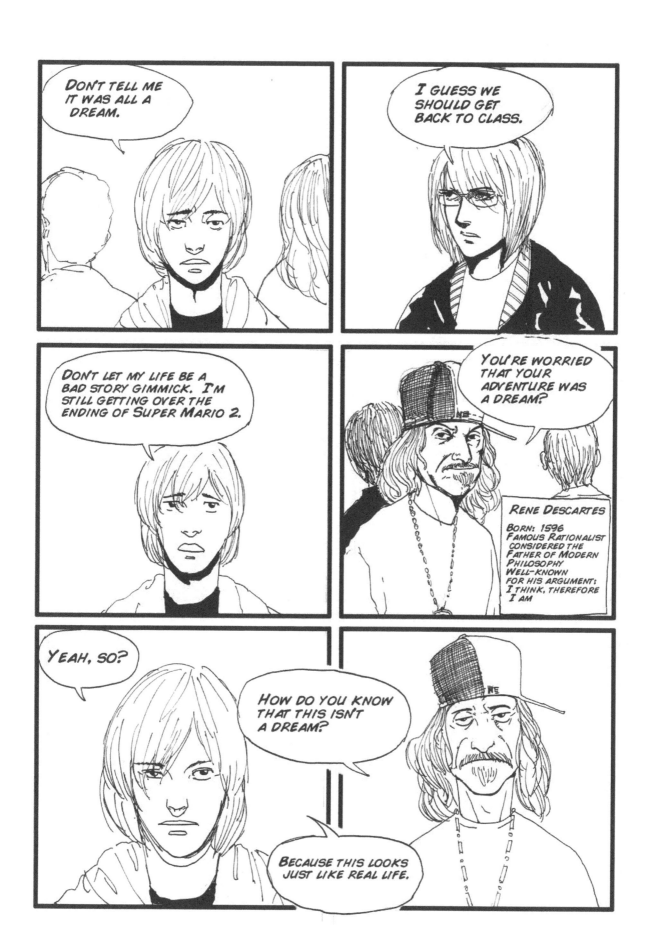

BUT LIFE DOESN'T PRESENT FOUR OPTIONS AND ASK US TO PICK ONE! THE IMPORTANT SKILL IS FIGURING OUT WHAT THE OPTIONS ARE IN THE FIRST PLACE.

THE TRADITIONAL TEACHER IS DEFEATED!

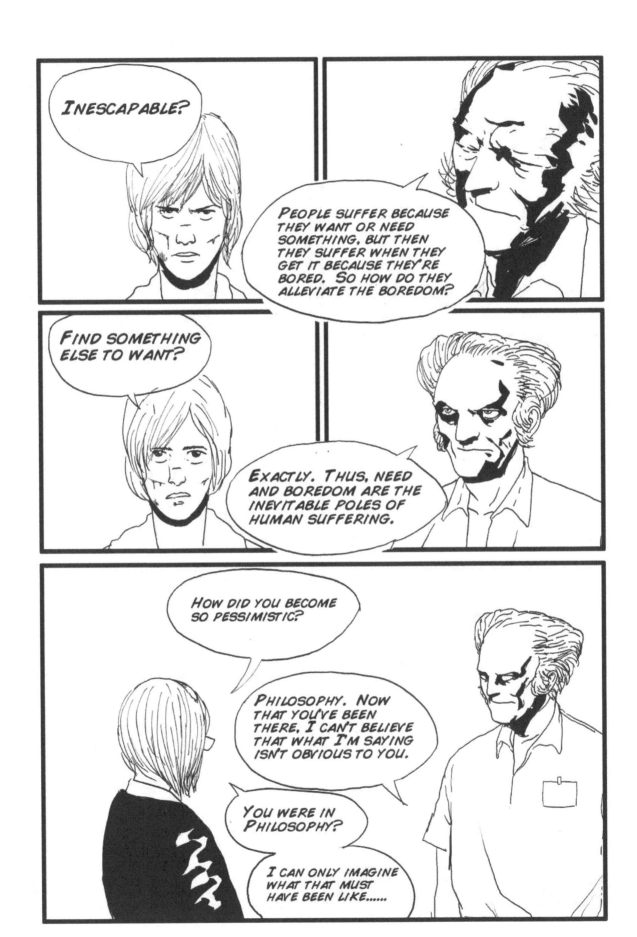

Well, here we go.

Wait, do we have to?

Yes.

Why?

Remember the Seasoned Skeptic?

Oh, yeah. I don't ever want to become that.

431

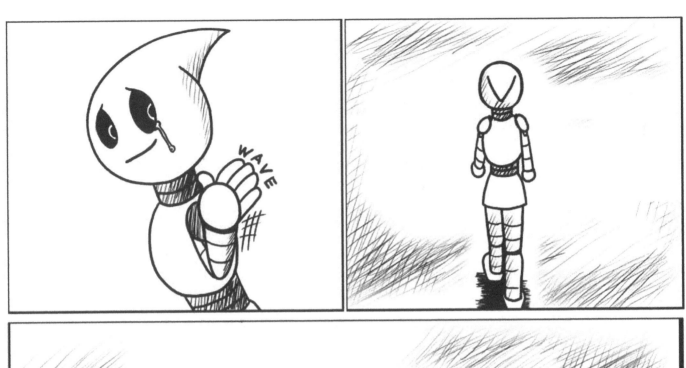

435

439

THIS PAGE
INTENTIONALLY
LEFT BLANK